MW00904288

Aris Brown and Career Day

Printed in the United States of America.

www.deshanaedmond.com

ISBN 978-1-73-557990-0

The artist used Adobe Photoshop to create the digital illustrations for this book.

Typography by Nathan Donald Jones

To God, thank you for creating us all with unlimited potential. For my son Aris, the inspiration behind this book series; you truly are the absolute BEST! To my husband Brett, thank you for all of your encouragement and for always seeing the greatest in me. For every child who desires to do great things in life.

-De'Shana' Edmond

To my husband Lesley, my kids Theo and Morgan, and my parents Marie Glenn and Arturo, thank you for always supporting me on what I dream to do and what I want to be

-Patricia M. Hung

Tomorrow is Career Day, and Aris is so excited! Aris and his friends get to share with their class what they would like to do in life.

At lunch, Echo asked Aris what he wanted to be.

Aris said, “I want to be a motivational speaker, just like my dad!”

During recess, Miguel said he hoped to be a police officer.

Aris told Miguel he wanted to be an
author of many books.

After storytime, Lahya said she was going to be a doctor.

Aris shared with her that he desired to be a language interpreter.

At the end of the day, while getting their coats, Sergey told everyone that he planned to be a world traveler.

Aris told everyone that he was going to be a professional musician.

"But I thought you said you wanted to be a motivational speaker," said Echo.

"He told me he was going to b an author of many books! exclaimed Migue

"What about a language interpreter?" asked Lahya.

All of Aris's friends looked confused. "So," said Echo. "Which one are you going to pick?" "Yeah!" said Sergey. "You have to choose one!"

When Aris returned home from school, he was sad about only being able to choose one thing to pursue.

Dad asked, "What's wrong, son? I thought you would be excited about Career Day tomorrow?"

"I was excited," said Aris, "until my friends told me that I had to choose one thing to do in life. But you always tell me I can do anything."

"Yes, son, you are right. You have **potential!**"

"What's potential?" asked Aris.

"Potential," replied Dad, "means that you have the ability to be anything that you want to be. You can do whatever you are passionate about!"

Dad got close to Aris's face and held his shoulders with a big smile and said, **"When you put limits on what you can be, then you limit what you will be."**

"So, does that mean I can be all the things I told my friends?" asked Aris.
"Yes!" said Dad. "It absolutely does!"

"But what about what my friends said? They think they can only choose one thing."

"Well, son maybe you can remind them that they also have potential."

The next day, Aris went to school with his project, ready to share with his friends and teacher.

When it was his turn, Aris opened up his poster board with four different careers.

"But he can't do that!" shouted Miguel. "He has to pick one."

Aris's teacher Mr. James responded, "Aris, why don't you tell us why you chose four careers."

With a huge smile on his face, Aris replied, "I chose to do these things because I like them a lot. I believe I have unlimited potential to be anything I want. So, why should I choose just one career?"

Aris's classmates looked puzzled.
"Aris is right class," said Mr. James.
"Huh?" the students replied.

Mr. James continued,
"I'm very proud of you, Aris. We all have the potential to be whatever we want to be in life. As long as we are focused on our goals, we will succeed."

"Well, I really love dancing. I've been dancing since I was three. I'm going to be a doctor and a dancer!" exclaimed Lahya.

"I like cooking. My mom says I cook better than my dad.

Does that mean I can own a restaurant and be a police officer?" asked Miguel. "It sure does!" said Mr. James.

The entire class began to chatter with excitement, talking about all the things they considered being before they decided to make one choice.

"All right class," said Mr. James, trying to calm the class down. "This is a very exciting day! I'm elated that you all are so thrilled about your future. Let's thank Aris for reminding us of our unlimited potential!"

The entire class cheered for Aris.
After the presentation, all of the students began to think about other things they wanted to do.

So, what about you?
You also have unlimited potential.

What do you love to do?

Motivational speaker

Artist Language interpreter

Dancer Professional athlete Gymnast

Professional musician

Movie producer

Librarian Author Five star che

World traveler

Police officer

Fire Fighter Actor

Doctor Video game develope

Singer

President Scientis

Principal

Illustrator

Bodybuilder Philanthropist

Photographer TV producer Hair Designe

Animator

Pastor Teacher Nurse midwif

Entrepreneur Counselo

Choreographer

Personal trainer Activist

CPSIA information can be obtained
at www.ICGtesting.com
Printed in the USA
BVHW020551051020
590283BV00003B/7